THE WALKERS

by Jim Watson

ISBN 1 85284 122 2

Published by Cicerone Press
Police Square,
Milnthorpe,
Cumbria

Meet the family...

Stroll'n' Norman Walker
Walkoholic teamboss. Leads tirelessly from the front, lantern jaw jutting fearlessly into the wild uncharted regions of the countryside. That's what he thinks anyway.

Kevin 'megabyte' Walker
The problem son. Eats anything without complaint, loves walking and his sister, and generally refuses to behave like a normal teenager.

Avril Walker
Fights a endless campaign to keep the family on the straight and narrow across the roughest of terrain. Worries constantly about Norman and the kids, but who wouldn't?

Terri, 'leen Walker
Aged eight - going on sixteen. Walks only to the sound of her own drum.

Walker dogs Unfaithful companions that keep running away from home. Taken into care, they are counselled by teams of social workers for deep trauma brought on by over-exposure to prolonged exercise.

HOW LONG HAS DAD BEEN
INTO BUNJEE JUMPING?

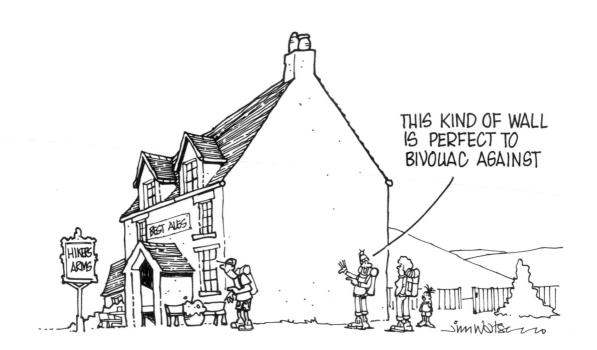

CURSE THE HAYFEVER!

REMIND ME NOT TO
MAKE CAMP IN THE
DARK AGAIN !

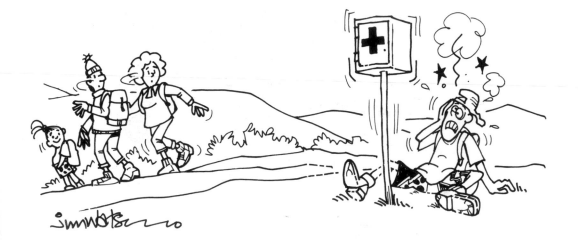